KU-215-317

2018 SQA Specimen and Past Papers with Answers

National 5
MATHEMATICS

2017 & 2018 Exams
and 2017 Specimen Question Paper

HODDER
GIBSON
AN HACHETTE UK COMPANY

This book contains the official SQA 2017 and 2018 Exams, and the 2017 Specimen Question Paper for National 5 Mathematics, with associated SQA-approved answers modified from the official marking instructions that accompany the paper.

In addition the book contains study skills advice. This advice has been specially commissioned by Hodder Gibson, and has been written by experienced senior teachers and examiners in line with the new National 5 syllabus and assessment outlines. This is not SQA material but has been devised to provide further guidance for National 5 examinations.

Hodder Gibson is grateful to the copyright holders, as credited on the final page of the Answer section, for permission to use their material. Every effort has been made to trace the copyright holders and to obtain their permission for the use of copyright material. Hodder Gibson will be happy to receive information allowing us to rectify any error or omission in future editions.

Hachette UK's policy is to use papers that are natural, renewable and recyclable products and made from wood grown in sustainable forests. The logging and manufacturing processes are expected to conform to the environmental regulations of the country of origin.

Orders: please contact Bookpoint Ltd, 130 Park Drive, Milton Park, Abingdon, Oxon OX14 4SE. Telephone: (44) 01235 827827. Fax: (44) 01235 400454. Lines are open 9.00–5.00, Monday to Saturday, with a 24-hour message answering service. Visit our website at www.hoddereducation.co.uk. Hodder Gibson can also be contacted directly at hoddergibson@hodder.co.uk

This collection first published in 2018 by
Hodder Gibson, an imprint of Hodder Education,
An Hachette UK Company
211 St Vincent Street
Glasgow G2 5QY

National 5 2017 and 2018 Exam Papers and Answers; 2017 Specimen Question Paper and Answers © Scottish Qualifications Authority. Study Skills section © Hodder Gibson. All rights reserved. Apart from any use permitted under UK copyright law, no part of this publication may be reproduced or transmitted in any form or by any means, electronic or mechanical, including photocopying and recording, or held within any information storage and retrieval system, without permission in writing from the publisher or under licence from the Copyright Licensing Agency Limited. Further details of such licences (for reprographic reproduction) may be obtained from the Copyright Licensing Agency Limited, www.cla.co.uk

Typeset by Aptara, Inc.

Printed in the UK

A catalogue record for this title is available from the British Library

ISBN: 978-1-5104-5498-9

2 1

2019 2018

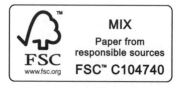

Introduction

National 5 Mathematics

This book of SQA past papers contains the question papers used in the 2017 and 2018 exams (with answers at the back of the book). A specimen question paper reflecting the content and duration of the exam in 2018 is also included.

All of the question papers included in the book (2017, 2018 and the specimen question paper) provide excellent representative exam practice for the final exams. Using these papers as part of your revision will help you to develop the vital skills and techniques needed for the exam, and will help you to identify any knowledge gaps you may have.

It is always a very good idea to refer to SQA's website for the most up-to-date course specification documents. These are available at https://www.sqa.org.uk/sqa/47419

The course

The National 5 Mathematics course aims to enable you to develop the ability to:

- select and apply mathematical techniques in a variety of mathematical and real-life situations
- manipulate abstract terms in order to solve problems and to generalise
- interpret, communicate and manage information in mathematical form
- use mathematical language and explore mathematical ideas.

Before starting this course you should already have the knowledge, understanding and skills required to achieve a good pass in National 4 Mathematics and/or be proficient in equivalent experiences and outcomes. This course enables you to further develop your knowledge, understanding and skills in algebra, geometry, trigonometry, numeracy, statistics and reasoning. The course content is summarised below.

Algebra	Geometry		Trigonometry
<ul><li>Expanding brackets</li><li>Factorising</li><li>Completing the square</li><li>Algebraic fractions</li><li>Equation of straight line</li><li>Functional notation</li><li>Equations and inequations</li><li>Simultaneous equations</li><li>Change of subject of formulae</li><li>Graphs of quadratic functions</li><li>Quadratic equations and discriminant</li></ul>	<ul><li>Gradient</li><li>Volume</li><li>Properties of shapes</li><li>Vectors and 3D coordinates</li></ul>	<ul><li>Arc and sector of circle</li><li>Pythagoras' theorem</li><li>Similarity</li></ul>	<ul><li>Graphs</li><li>Equations</li><li>Identities</li><li>Area of triangle, sine rule, cosine rule, bearings</li></ul>
	Numeracy		**Statistics**
	<ul><li>Surds</li><li>Indices and scientific notation</li><li>Rounding (significant figures)</li><li>Percentages</li><li>Fractions</li></ul>		<ul><li>Semi-interquartile range, standard deviation</li><li>Scattergraphs; equation of line of best fit</li></ul>
Reasoning			
<ul><li>Interpreting a situation where mathematics can be used and identifying a strategy.</li><li>Explaining a solution and/or relating it to context.</li></ul>			

Assessment

The course assessment is an examination comprising two question papers.

The number of marks and the times allotted for the examination papers are as follows:

Paper 1 (non-calculator)	50 marks	1 hour 15 minutes
Paper 2	60 marks	1 hour 50 minutes

The course assessment is graded A-D, the grade being determined by the total mark you score in the examination.

Some tips for achieving a good mark

- **DOING** maths questions is the most effective use of your study time. You will benefit much more from spending 30 minutes doing maths questions than spending several hours copying out notes or reading a maths textbook.

- Practise doing the type of questions that are likely to appear in the exam. Work through these practice papers and similar questions from past Credit Level and Intermediate 2 papers. Use the marking instructions to check your answers and to understand what the examiners are looking for. Ask your teacher for help if you get stuck.

- **SHOW ALL WORKING CLEARLY.** The instructions on the front of the exam paper state that "To earn full marks you must show your working in your answers". A "correct" answer with no working may only be awarded partial marks or even no marks at all. An incomplete answer will be awarded marks for any appropriate working. Attempt every question, even if you are not sure whether you are correct or not. Your solution may contain working which will gain some marks. A blank response is certain to be awarded no marks. Never score out working unless you have something better to replace it with.

- Communication is very important in presenting solutions to questions. Diagrams are often a good way of conveying information and enabling markers to understand your working. Where a diagram is included in a question, it is often good practice to copy it and show the results of your working on the copy.
- In Paper 1, you have to carry out calculations without a calculator. Candidates' performance in number skills is often disappointing, and costs many of them valuable marks. Ensure that you practise your number skills regularly, especially within questions testing Course content.
- In Paper 2, you will be allowed to use a calculator. Always use **your own** calculator. Different calculators often function in slightly different ways, so make sure that you know how to operate yours. Having to use a calculator that you are unfamiliar with on the day of the exam will disadvantage you.
- Prepare thoroughly to tackle questions from **all** parts of the course. Numerical and algebraic fractions, graphs of quadratic fractions, surds, indices and trigonometric identities are topics that often cause candidates problems. Be prepared to put extra effort into mastering these topics.

Some common errors to avoid

	Common error	Correct answer
Converse of Pythagoras' Theorem e.g. Prove that triangle ABC is right angled. A 3 5 B 4 C	Don't start by assuming what you are trying to prove is true. $AC^2 = AB^2 + BC^2$ $AC^2 = 3^2 + 4^2 = 9 + 16 = 25$ $AC = \sqrt{25} = 5$ so triangle ABC is right angled by the Converse of Pythagoras' Theorem.	Don't state that $AC^2 = AB^2 + BC^2$ until you have the evidence to prove that it is true. $AC^2 = 5^2 = 25$ $AB^2 + BC^2 = 3^2 + 4^2 = 9 + 16 = 25$ so $AC^2 = AB^2 + BC^2$ so triangle ABC is right angled by the Converse of Pythagoras' Theorem.
Similarity (area and volume) e.g. 5cm 10cm Theses cylinders are mathematically similar. The volume of the small one is 60cm^3. Calculate the volume of the large one.	Don't use the linear scale factor to calculate the volume (or area) of a similar shape. Scale factor = 2 Volume = 2 × 60 = 120cm^3	Remember that volume factor = (linear factor)^3 area factor = (linear factor)^2 Scale factor = 2 Volume = 2^3 × 60 = 480cm^3
Reverse use of percentage e.g. After a 5% pay rise, Ann now earns £252 per week. Calculate her weekly pay before the rise.	Increase = 5% of old pay **NOT** 5% of new pay Increase = 5% of £252 = £12·60 Old pay = £252 - £12·60 = £239·40	New pay = (100% + 5%) of old pay New pay = 105% of old pay = £252 1% of old pay = £252 ÷ 105 = £2·40 Old pay = 100% = £2·40 × 100 = £240
Interpreting statistics e.g. Jack and Jill sat tests in the same eight subjects. Jack's mean mark was 76 and his standard deviation was 13. Jill's mean mark was 59 and her standard deviation was 21. Make two valid comments comparing the performance of Jack and Jill in the tests.	This answer does not show that you **understand** the meaning of mean and standard deviation. Jack has a higher mean mark but a lower standard deviation than Jill.	Your interpretation of the figures must show that you **understand** that mean is an average and that standard deviation is a measure of spread. On average Jack performed better than Jill as his mean mark was higher. Jack's performance was more consistent than Jill's as the standard deviation of his marks was lower.

Good luck!

Remember that the rewards for passing National 5 Mathematics are well worth it! Your pass will help you get the future you want for yourself. In the exam, be confident in your own ability, if you're not sure how to answer a question trust your instincts and just give it a go anyway – keep calm and don't panic! GOOD LUCK!

Study Skills – what you need to know to pass exams!

General exam revision: 20 top tips

When preparing for exams, it is easy to feel unsure of where to start or how to revise. This guide to general exam revision provides a good starting place, and, as these are very general tips, they can be applied to all your exams.

1. Start revising in good time.

Don't leave revision until the last minute – this will make you panic and it will be difficult to learn. Make a revision timetable that counts down the weeks to go.

2. Work to a study plan.

Set up sessions of work spread through the weeks ahead. Make sure each session has a focus and a clear purpose. What will you study, when and why? Be realistic about what you can achieve in each session, and don't be afraid to adjust your plans as needed.

3. Make sure you know exactly when your exams are.

Get your exam dates from the SQA website and use the timetable builder tool to create your own exam schedule. You will also get a personalised timetable from your school, but this might not be until close to the exam period.

4. Make sure that you know the topics that make up each course.

Studying is easier if material is in manageable chunks – why not use the SQA topic headings or create your own from your class notes? Ask your teacher for help on this if you are not sure.

5. Break the chunks up into even smaller bits.

The small chunks should be easier to cope with. Remember that they fit together to make larger ideas. Even the process of chunking down will help!

6. Ask yourself these key questions for each course:

- Are all topics compulsory or are there choices?
- Which topics seem to come up time and time again?
- Which topics are your strongest and which are your weakest?

Use your answers to these questions to work out how much time you will need to spend revising each topic.

7. Make sure you know what to expect in the exam.

The subject-specific introduction to this book will help with this. Make sure you can answer these questions:

- How is the paper structured?
- How much time is there for each part of the exam?
- What types of question are involved? These will vary depending on the subject so read the subject-specific section carefully.

8. Past papers are a vital revision tool!

Use past papers to support your revision wherever possible. This book contains the answers and mark schemes too – refer to these carefully when checking your work. Using the mark scheme is useful; even if you don't manage to get all the marks available first time when you first practise, it helps you identify how to extend and develop your answers to get more marks next time – and of course, in the real exam.

9. Use study methods that work well for you.

People study and learn in different ways. Reading and looking at diagrams suits some students. Others prefer to listen and hear material – what about reading out loud or getting a friend or family member to do this for you? You could also record and play back material.

10. There are three tried and tested ways to make material stick in your long-term memory:

- Practising – e.g. rehearsal, repeating
- Organising – e.g. making drawings, lists, diagrams, tables, memory aids
- Elaborating – e.g. incorporating the material into a story or an imagined journey

11. Learn actively.

Most people prefer to learn actively – for example, making notes, highlighting, redrawing and redrafting, making up memory aids, or writing past paper answers. A good way to stay engaged and inspired is to mix and match these methods – find the combination that best suits you. This is likely to vary depending on the topic or subject.

12. Be an expert.

Be sure to have a few areas in which you feel you are an expert. This often works because at least some of them will come up, which can boost confidence.

13. Try some visual methods.

Use symbols, diagrams, charts, flashcards, post-it notes etc. Don't forget – the brain takes in chunked images more easily than loads of text.

14. Remember – practice makes perfect.

Work on difficult areas again and again. Look and read – then test yourself. You cannot do this too much.

15. Try past papers against the clock.

Practise writing answers in a set time. This is a good habit from the start but is especially important when you get closer to exam time.

16. Collaborate with friends.

Test each other and talk about the material – this can really help. Two brains are better than one! It is amazing how talking about a problem can help you solve it.

17. Know your weaknesses.

Ask your teacher for help to identify what you don't know. Try to do this as early as possible. If you are having trouble, it is probably with a difficult topic, so your teacher will already be aware of this – most students will find it tough.

18. Have your materials organised and ready.

Know what is needed for each exam:

- Do you need a calculator or a ruler?
- Should you have pencils as well as pens?
- Will you need water or paper tissues?

19. Make full use of school resources.

Find out what support is on offer:

- Are there study classes available?
- When is the library open?
- When is the best time to ask for extra help?
- Can you borrow textbooks, study guides, past papers, etc.?
- Is school open for Easter revision?

20. Keep fit and healthy!

Try to stick to a routine as much as possible, including with sleep. If you are tired, sluggish or dehydrated, it is difficult to see how concentration is even possible. Combine study with relaxation, drink plenty of water, eat sensibly, and get fresh air and exercise – all these things will help more than you could imagine. Good luck!

NATIONAL 5

2017

FOR OFFICIAL USE

N5

National Qualifications 2017

Mark

X747/75/01

Mathematics
Paper 1
(Non-Calculator)

FRIDAY, 5 MAY

1:00 PM — 2:00 PM

Fill in these boxes and read what is printed below.

Full name of centre

Town

Forename(s)

Surname

Number of seat

Date of birth

Day	Month	Year	Scottish candidate number

Total marks — 40

Attempt ALL questions.

You may NOT use a calculator.

Full credit will be given only to solutions which contain appropriate working.

State the units for your answer where appropriate.

Write your answers clearly in the spaces provided in this booklet. Additional space for answers is provided at the end of this booklet. If you use this space you must clearly identify the question number you are attempting.

Use **blue** or **black** ink.

Before leaving the examination room you must give this book to the Invigilator; if you do not, you may lose all the marks for this paper.

FORMULAE LIST

The roots of $ax^2 + bx + c = 0$ are $x = \dfrac{-b \pm \sqrt{(b^2 - 4ac)}}{2a}$

Sine rule: $\dfrac{a}{\sin A} = \dfrac{b}{\sin B} = \dfrac{c}{\sin C}$

Cosine rule: $a^2 = b^2 + c^2 - 2bc\cos A$ or $\cos A = \dfrac{b^2 + c^2 - a^2}{2bc}$

Area of a triangle: $A = \tfrac{1}{2}ab\sin C$

Volume of a sphere: $V = \tfrac{4}{3}\pi r^3$

Volume of a cone: $V = \tfrac{1}{3}\pi r^2 h$

Volume of a pyramid: $V = \tfrac{1}{3}Ah$

Standard deviation: $s = \sqrt{\dfrac{\Sigma(x - \bar{x})^2}{n-1}}$

or $s = \sqrt{\dfrac{\Sigma x^2 - \dfrac{(\Sigma x)^2}{n}}{n-1}}$, where n is the sample size.

MARKS | DO NOT WRITE IN THIS MARGIN

Total marks — 40

Attempt ALL questions

1. Given that $f(x) = x^2 + 3x$, evaluate $f(-5)$.   2

$$-5^2 + 3(-5)$$

$$= 25 - 15$$

$$= \underline{10}$$

2. The number of calls received by the police was recorded over 10 days.
   The results are shown below.

   198   216   218   230   232   247   248   250   265   267

   Find the semi-interquartile range of this data.   2

   198   216   218   230   232,   247   248   250   265 267

   Q1   234.5   Q3

   Q2

   $$SIQR = \frac{Q3 - Q1}{2}$$

   $$= \frac{32}{2}$$

   $$= \underline{16}$$

[Turn over

Page three

MARKS | DO NOT WRITE IN THIS MARGIN

3. Evaluate $1\frac{5}{6} \div \frac{3}{4}$.

Give your answer in its simplest form.

2

$$\frac{11}{6} \div \frac{3}{4}$$

$$= \frac{6}{11} \times \frac{4}{3} = \frac{24}{33}$$

4. Expand and simplify $(2x+3)(x^2-4x+1)$.

3

$$3x^2 - 12x + 3 + 2x^3 - 12x + 3$$

$$2x^3 + 3x^2 - 24x + 6$$

MARKS | DO NOT WRITE IN THIS MARGIN

5. The diagram shows a square-based pyramid placed on top of a cube, relative to the coordinate axes.

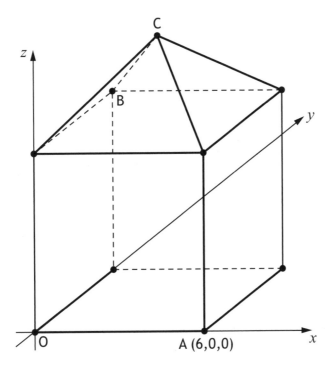

The height of the pyramid is half of the height of the cube.

A is the point (6,0,0).

The point C is directly above the centre of the base.

Write down the coordinates of B and C.

2

$B = (0, 6, 6)$

$C = (3, 3, 9)$

[Turn over

MARKS | DO NOT WRITE IN THIS MARGIN

6. The diagram below shows the straight line joining points A and B.

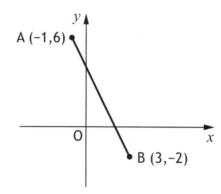

Find the equation of the line AB.

Give the equation in its simplest form.

3

$$m = \frac{y^2 - y^1}{x^2 - x^1}$$

$$= \frac{6 - (-2)}{-1 - 3}$$

$$= \frac{8}{-4} = -2$$

$$y = mx + c$$

$$y = -2x + c$$

$$6 = -2 \times x - 1 + c$$

$$6 = 2x + c$$

ans

$$c = 4$$

$$y = 2x + 4$$

7. In triangle DEF:

- DE = 8 centimetres

- EF = 12 centimetres

- $\sin E = \dfrac{2}{3}$

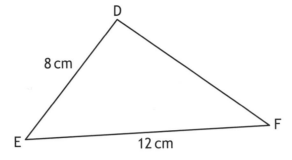

Calculate the area of triangle DEF.   2

$$\frac{1}{2} \times 12 \times 8 \frac{2}{3}$$

$$0.5 \times 12 \times 8 = 48$$

$$48 \div 3 = 16 \times 2 = 32$$

[Turn over

Page seven

MARKS | DO NOT WRITE IN THIS MARGIN

8. Solve, algebraically, the inequality

$$19 + x > 15 + 3(x - 2).$$

3

$19 + x > 15 + 3(x - 2)$

$19 + x > 15 + 3x - 6$

MARKS | DO NOT WRITE IN THIS MARGIN

9. In the diagram shown below:

- ABE is a tangent to the circle centre O

- Angle DBE is 58°

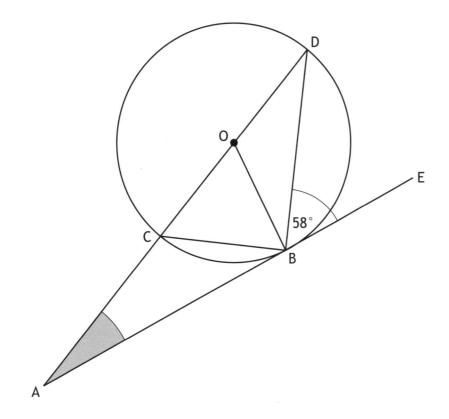

Calculate the size of angle CAB.   3

[Turn over

10. Change the subject of the formula $F = \dfrac{t^2 + 4b}{c}$ to b.

3

$$CF = \sqrt{\dfrac{t}{4}} = b$$

$$FC = t^2 + 4b$$

$$4b = FC - t^2$$

$$b = FC - t^2$$

11. Express $\dfrac{3}{a^2} - \dfrac{2}{a}$, $a \neq 0$, as a single fraction in its simplest form.

2

MARKS | DO NOT WRITE IN THIS MARGIN

12. Gym members are asked to fill out a questionnaire to rate the quality of service provided.

They are asked to give a rating on a scale of 1 to 6.

The ratings given by five members were as follows:

$$1 \quad 4 \quad 6 \quad 3 \quad 6$$

In its simplest form, the standard deviation of these ratings can be written as $\dfrac{a\sqrt{b}}{2}$.

Find the values of a and b.   4

$$m = 20 \div 5 = 4$$

x	$(x - \bar{x})$	$(x-\bar{x})^2$
1	-3	9
4	0	0
6	2	4
3	-1	1
6	2	4
		$\Sigma 18$

$$Sd = \sqrt{\frac{(x-x)^2}{n-1}}$$

$$= \sqrt{\frac{18}{4}}$$

$$= \underline{4.5}$$

[Turn over

MARKS | DO NOT WRITE IN THIS MARGIN

13. The graph below shows two straight lines with the equations:

- $3x - y = 2$

- $x + 3y = 19$

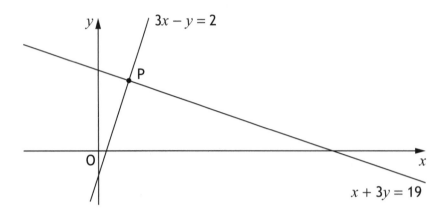

The lines intersect at the point P.

Find, **algebraically**, the coordinates of P.

3

$$3x - y = 2 \quad ①$$
$$x + 3y = 19 \quad ②$$
$$3x + 9y = 57 \quad ③ \quad ②×3$$
_____
$$8y =$$

MARKS | DO NOT WRITE IN THIS MARGIN

14. The graph below shows a parabola with equation of the form $y = (x + a)^2 + b$.

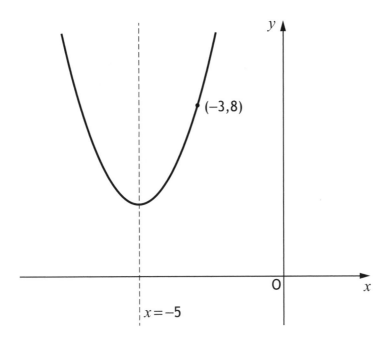

The equation of the axis of symmetry of the parabola is $x = -5$.

(a) State the value of a.   1

$$a = 5$$

The point $(-3, 8)$ lies on the parabola.

(b) Calculate the value of b.   2

$$8 = (-3 + 5)^2 + b$$

$$2^2 = 4$$

$$8 = 4 + b$$

$$b = 2$$

[Turn over for next question

Page thirteen

MARKS | DO NOT WRITE IN THIS MARGIN

15. In the diagram below:

- TS is parallel to QR
- TS = 5 centimetres
- QR = 7 centimetres
- SR = 2·6 centimetres

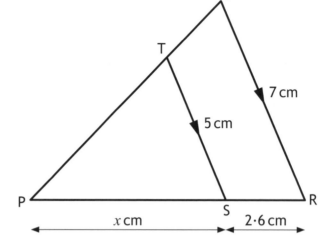

The length of PS is x centimetres.

Calculate the value of x.

3

[END OF QUESTION PAPER]

ADDITIONAL SPACE FOR ANSWERS

ADDITIONAL SPACE FOR ANSWERS

FOR OFFICIAL USE

N5

National
Qualifications
2017

Mark

X747/75/02

Mathematics
Paper 2

FRIDAY, 5 MAY

2:20 PM — 3:50 PM

Fill in these boxes and read what is printed below.

Full name of centre

Town

Forename(s)

Surname

Number of seat

Date of birth

Day   Month   Year

Scottish candidate number

Total marks — 50

Attempt ALL questions.

You may use a calculator.

Full credit will be given only to solutions which contain appropriate working.

State the units for your answer where appropriate.

Write your answers clearly in the spaces provided in this booklet. Additional space for answers is provided at the end of this booklet. If you use this space you must clearly identify the question number you are attempting.

Use **blue** or **black** ink.

Before leaving the examination room you must give this book to the Invigilator; if you do not, you may lose all the marks for this paper.

FORMULAE LIST

The roots of $ax^2 + bx + c = 0$ are $x = \dfrac{-b \pm \sqrt{(b^2 - 4ac)}}{2a}$

Sine rule: $\dfrac{a}{\sin A} = \dfrac{b}{\sin B} = \dfrac{c}{\sin C}$

Cosine rule: $a^2 = b^2 + c^2 - 2bc\cos A$ or $\cos A = \dfrac{b^2 + c^2 - a^2}{2bc}$

Area of a triangle: $A = \frac{1}{2}ab\sin C$

Volume of a sphere: $V = \frac{4}{3}\pi r^3$

Volume of a cone: $V = \frac{1}{3}\pi r^2 h$

Volume of a pyramid: $V = \frac{1}{3}Ah$

Standard deviation: $s = \sqrt{\dfrac{\Sigma(x - \bar{x})^2}{n - 1}}$

or $s = \sqrt{\dfrac{\Sigma x^2 - \dfrac{(\Sigma x)^2}{n}}{n - 1}}$, where n is the sample size.

MARKS

DO NOT WRITE IN THIS MARGIN

Total marks — 50

Attempt ALL questions

1. Find $|\mathbf{v}|$, the magnitude of vector $\mathbf{v} = \begin{pmatrix} 18 \\ -14 \\ 3 \end{pmatrix}$.

2

$$|v| = \sqrt{18^2 + (-14)^2 + 3^2}$$

$$= \sqrt{529}$$

2. A necklace is valued at £1200.

Its value is expected to increase by 4·5% per year over the next 3 years.

Calculate the expected value of the necklace after this time.

Give your answer to the nearest pound.

3

£1369

[Turn over

Page three

MARKS | DO NOT WRITE IN THIS MARGIN

3. A piece of land is in the shape of a triangle as shown.

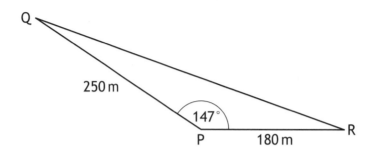

- PQ = 250 metres
- PR = 180 metres
- angle QPR = 147°

The owner wishes to build a fence along the side QR.

Calculate the length of the fence.

3

$a^2 = b^2 + c^2 - 2 \times b \times b \, \cos A$

$P = 180^2 + 250^2 - 2 \times 180 \times 250 \times \cos 147$

$= \sqrt{170380 \cdot 3511}$

$= 412 \cdot 8 \text{ metres (1dp)}$

MARKS | DO NOT WRITE IN THIS MARGIN

4. Solve the equation $2x^2 + 5x - 4 = 0$.

    Give your answers correct to one decimal place.

    3

$$\frac{-b \pm \sqrt{b^2 - 4ac}}{2a}$$

$$\frac{-5 \pm \sqrt{5^2 - 4(2) - (4)}}{2(2)}$$

$$\frac{-5 \pm \sqrt{57}}{4} =$$

5. A theatre group sold 4830 tickets for their show.

    This was 15% more than they sold last year.

    How many tickets did they sell last year?

    3

$$0.85 \times 4830$$

$$= 4106 \text{ . Cnearest whole number}$$

[Turn over

Page five

6. A spherical sweet is made by coating a caramel sphere evenly with chocolate.

A cross-section of the sweet is shown below.

3 mm

24 mm

The diameter of the sweet is 24 millimetres and the thickness of the chocolate coating is 3 millimetres.

Calculate the volume of the chocolate coating.

Give your answer correct to 3 significant figures.

5

$V_1 = \frac{4}{3} \pi r^3$

$= \frac{4}{3} \pi 12^3$

$= 7238.23$

$V_2 = \frac{4}{3} \pi r^3$

$= \frac{4}{3} \pi 9^3$

$= 3053.62$

$v^1 - v^2 = 4180 \, m^3$

MARKS | DO NOT WRITE IN THIS MARGIN

7. Triangles A and B are shown below.

The triangles are placed together to form the larger triangle shown below.

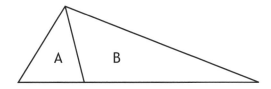

Is this larger triangle right-angled?

Justify your answer.

3

$$8^2 + 19^2 = 425$$

$$22^2 = 484$$

So $8^2 + 19^2 \neq 22^2$, this triangle is not right angled.

[Turn over

MARKS | DO NOT WRITE IN THIS MARGIN

8. In the diagram below, $\overrightarrow{RQ}$ and $\overrightarrow{PQ}$ represent the vectors **c** and **d** respectively.

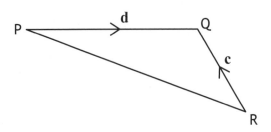

(a) Express $\overrightarrow{PR}$ in terms of **c** and **d**.   1

The line QP is extended to T.

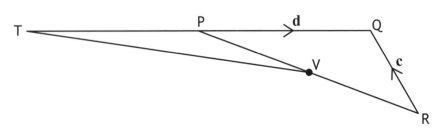

- TP = PQ
- V is the midpoint of PR

(b) Express $\overrightarrow{TV}$ in terms of **c** and **d**.

   Give your answer in simplest form.   2

MARKS | DO NOT WRITE IN THIS MARGIN

9. (a) Factorise $4x^2 - 25$.

1

$(2x - 5)(2x + 5)$

(b) Hence simplify $\dfrac{4x^2 - 25}{2x^2 - x - 10}$.

3

[Turn over

10. In the diagram below D, E and F represent the positions of Dunbridge, Earlsford and Fairtown respectively.

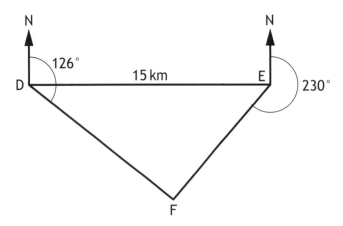

Dunbridge is 15 kilometres west of Earlsford.

From Dunbridge, the bearing of Fairtown is 126°.

From Earlsford the bearing of Fairtown is 230°.

Calculate the distance between Dunbridge and Fairtown.

Do not use a scale drawing.

4

MARKS | DO NOT WRITE IN THIS MARGIN

11. A straight line has equation $3x - 5y - 10 = 0$.

Find the gradient of this line.

2

$y = mx + c$

$y = .10 \, x + c$

$-5y = -10x \, (3) + c$

$-5y = -30 + c$

$y = -6$

12. Express $\dfrac{1}{\sqrt[3]{x}}$ in the form x^n.

2

$x^{-\frac{1}{3}}$

[Turn over

13. Two identical shapes are used to form a logo.

Each shape is part of a circle.

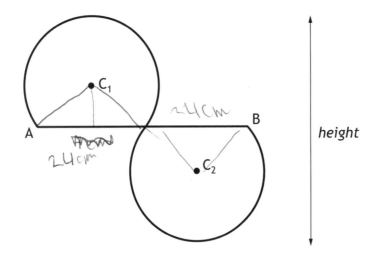

- The circles have centres C_1 and C_2.
- The radius of each circle is 14 centimetres.
- The logo has half-turn symmetry about the mid-point of AB.
- AB is 48 centimetres long.

Calculate the height of the logo.

4

$$14^2 - 12^2 = \sqrt{52}$$
$$= 7.2$$

$$h = 7.2 + 14 = 21.2$$
$$h = 2 \times 21.2 = 42.4$$

MARKS | DO NOT WRITE IN THIS MARGIN

14. The diagram below shows part of a circle, centre O.

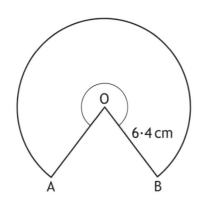

6·4 cm

A   B

The radius of the circle is 6·4 centimetres.

Major arc AB has length 31·5 centimetres.

Calculate the size of the reflex angle AOB.   3

$$31.5 = \frac{AOB}{360} \times \pi \times 12.8$$

$$= \frac{31.5 \times 380}{\pi \times 12.8}$$

$$= 282°$$

[Turn over

MARKS | DO NOT WRITE IN THIS MARGIN

15. A wind turbine has three blades as shown below.

Blade A

The height, h metres, of the tip of blade A above the ground in each rotation is given by

$$h = 40 + 23\cos x°, \qquad 0 \leq x < 360$$

where x is the angle blade A has turned clockwise from its vertical position.

(a) Calculate the height of the tip of blade A after it has turned through an angle of 60°.

1

MARKS | DO NOT WRITE IN THIS MARGIN

15.   (continued)

(b) Find the minimum height of the tip of blade A above the ground.   **1**

(c) Calculate the values of x for which the tip of blade A is 61 metres above the ground.   **4**

[END OF QUESTION PAPER]

MARKS | DO NOT WRITE IN THIS MARGIN

ADDITIONAL SPACE FOR ANSWERS

NATIONAL 5

2017 Specimen
Question Paper

FOR OFFICIAL USE

N5

Mark

National Qualifications
SPECIMEN ONLY

S847/75/01

Mathematics
Paper 1
(Non-Calculator)

Date — Not applicable

Duration — 1 hour 15 minutes

Fill in these boxes and read what is printed below.

Full name of centre

Town

Forename(s)

Surname

Number of seat

Date of birth

Day	Month	Year	Scottish candidate number

Total marks — 50

Attempt ALL questions.

You may NOT use a calculator.

To earn full marks you must show your working in your answers.

State the units for your answer where appropriate.

Write your answers clearly in the spaces provided in this booklet. Additional space for answers is provided at the end of this booklet. If you use this space you must clearly identify the question number you are attempting.

Use **blue** or **black** ink.

Before leaving the examination room you must give this booklet to the Invigilator; if you do not, you may lose all the marks for this paper.

FORMULAE LIST

The roots of $ax^2 + bx + c = 0$ are $x = \dfrac{-b \pm \sqrt{(b^2 - 4ac)}}{2a}$

Sine rule: $\dfrac{a}{\sin A} = \dfrac{b}{\sin B} = \dfrac{c}{\sin C}$

Cosine rule: $a^2 = b^2 + c^2 - 2bc\cos A$ or $\cos A = \dfrac{b^2 + c^2 - a^2}{2bc}$

Area of a triangle: $A = \frac{1}{2}ab\sin C$

Volume of a sphere: $V = \frac{4}{3}\pi r^3$

Volume of a cone: $V = \frac{1}{3}\pi r^2 h$

Volume of a pyramid: $V = \frac{1}{3}Ah$

Standard deviation: $s = \sqrt{\dfrac{\Sigma(x - \bar{x})^2}{n-1}}$

or $s = \sqrt{\dfrac{\Sigma x^2 - \dfrac{(\Sigma x)^2}{n}}{n-1}}$, where n is the sample size.

MARKS | DO NOT WRITE IN THIS MARGIN

Total marks — 50

Attempt ALL questions

1. Evaluate

$$2\frac{3}{8} \div \frac{5}{16}.$$

2

$$\frac{19}{8} \times \frac{16}{5} =$$

2. Solve algebraically the inequality

$$11 - 2(1 + 3x) < 39.$$

3

$$11 - 2 - 6x < 39$$

$$-6 < 30$$

[Turn over

MARKS | DO NOT WRITE IN THIS MARGIN

3. Two forces acting on a rocket are represented by vectors **u** and **v**.

$$\mathbf{u} = \begin{pmatrix} 2 \\ -5 \\ -3 \end{pmatrix} \text{ and } \mathbf{v} = \begin{pmatrix} 7 \\ 4 \\ -1 \end{pmatrix}.$$

Calculate $|\mathbf{u} + \mathbf{v}|$, the magnitude of the resultant force.

Express your answer as a surd in its simplest form.   3

$$\sqrt{2^2 (-5)^2 (-3)^2}$$

$$= 30$$

$$= 8$$

$$30 + 8 \quad 38$$

$$\begin{pmatrix} 9 \\ (-1) \\ 4 \end{pmatrix} = \sqrt{9^2 (-1)^2 4^2}$$

$$= 7\sqrt{2}$$

$$= 9.899494937$$

$$= 9.8$$

MARKS | DO NOT WRITE IN THIS MARGIN

4. The diagram below shows part of the graph of $y = ax^2$.

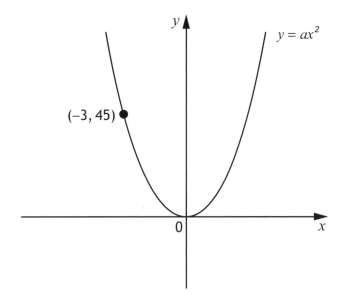

Find the value of a.　　2

$$y = ax^2$$

$$45 = 3^2 \times a$$

$$45 = 9a$$

$$a = 5$$

[Turn over

MARKS | DO NOT WRITE IN THIS MARGIN

5. Determine the nature of the roots of the function $f(x) = 7x^2 + 5x - 1$. 2

$$a \quad b \quad c$$

$$b^2 - 4ac$$

$$5^2 - 4(7)(-1)$$

$$25 + 28$$

$$= 53$$

as $b^2 - 4ac$ is more than 0, there are 2 real roots

MARKS | DO NOT WRITE IN THIS MARGIN

6. A cattle farmer records the weight of some of his calves.

The scattergraph shows the relationship between the age, A months, and the weight, W kilograms, of the calves.

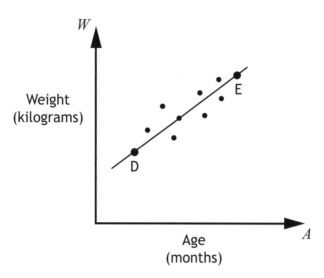

A line of best fit is drawn.

Point D represents a 3-month-old calf which weighs 100 kilograms.

Point E represents a 15-month-old calf which weighs 340 kilograms.

(a) Find the equation of the line of best fit in terms of A and W.

Give the equation in its simplest form.   **3**

(handwritten working:)

15, 340   3   100

$\dfrac{y_2 - y_1}{x_1 - x_2}$

$y = mx + c$

$100 = 20(3) + c$

$100 = 60 + c$

$\dfrac{340 - 100}{15 - 3}$

$c = 40$

$= \dfrac{240}{12}$

$= 20$

$W = 20A + 40$

[Turn over

MARKS | DO NOT WRITE IN THIS MARGIN

6. **(continued)**

(b) Use your equation from part (a) to estimate the weight of a 1-**year**-old calf.

Show your working. 1

MARKS | DO NOT WRITE IN THIS MARGIN

7. Ten couples took part in a dance competition.

The couples were given a score in each round.

The scores in the first round were

16   27   12   18   26   21   27   22   18   17

(a) Calculate the median and semi-interquartile range of these scores.   **3**

(b) In the second round, the median was 26 and the semi-interquartile range was 2·5.

Make two valid comparisons between the scores in the first and second rounds.   **2**

[Turn over

MARKS | DO NOT WRITE IN THIS MARGIN

8. Two groups of people go to a theatre.

Bill buys tickets for 5 adults and 3 children.

The total cost of his tickets is £158·25.

(a) Write down an equation to illustrate this information.   **1**

(b) Ben buys tickets for 3 adults and 2 children.

The total cost of his tickets is £98.

Write down an equation to illustrate this information.   **1**

(c) Calculate the cost of a ticket for an adult and the cost of a ticket for a child.   **4**

MARKS

9. 480 000 tickets were sold for a tennis tournament last year.

This represents 80% of all the available tickets.

Calculate the total number of tickets that were available for this tournament.   **3**

10. The function $f(x)$ is defined by $f(x) = \dfrac{2}{\sqrt{x}}$, $x > 0$.

Express $f(5)$ as a fraction with a rational denominator.   **2**

$$f(5) = \frac{2}{\sqrt{5}}$$

[Turn over

MARKS DO NOT WRITE IN THIS MARGIN

11. In the diagram, OABCDE is a regular hexagon with centre M.

Vectors **a** and **b** are represented by $\overrightarrow{OA}$ and $\overrightarrow{OB}$ respectively.

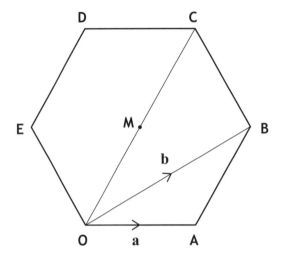

(a) Express $\overrightarrow{AB}$ in terms of **a** and **b**.   1

(b) Express $\overrightarrow{OC}$ in terms of **a** and **b**.   1

MARKS | DO NOT WRITE IN THIS MARGIN

12. Part of the graph of $y = a \sin bx°$ is shown in the diagram.

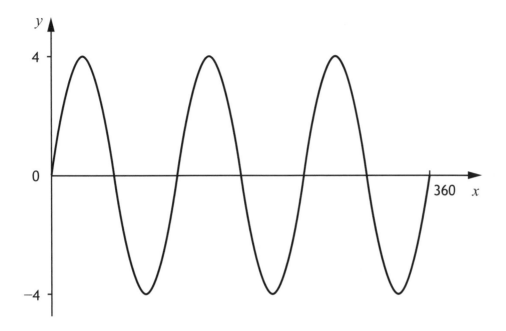

State the values of a and b.

2

$a = 4$

$b = 3$

[Turn over

MARKS | DO NOT WRITE IN THIS MARGIN

13. A parabola has equation $y = x^2 - 8x + 19$.

(a) Write the equation in the form $y = (x - p)^2 + q$.   **2**

$$y = (x - 4)^2 - 16 + 19$$
$$= (x - 4)^2 + 3$$

(b) Sketch the graph of $y = x^2 - 8x + 19$, showing the coordinates of the turning point and the point of intersection with the y-axis.   **3**

MARKS | DO NOT WRITE IN THIS MARGIN

14. Express

$$\frac{4}{x+2} - \frac{3}{x-4}, \qquad x \neq -2, x \neq 4$$

as a single fraction in its simplest form.

3

15. Simplify

$$\tan^2 x° \cos^2 x°.$$

Show your working.

2

[Turn over

MARKS

16. A cylindrical pipe has water in it as shown.

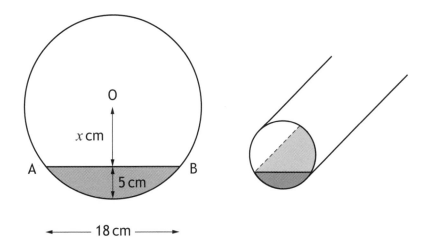

The depth of the water at the deepest point is 5 centimetres.

The width of the water surface, AB, is 18 centimetres.

The radius of the pipe is r centimetres.

The distance from the centre, O, of the pipe to the water surface is x centimetres.

(a) Write down an expression for x in terms of r.   1

(b) Calculate r, the radius of the pipe.   3

[END OF SPECIMEN QUESTION PAPER]

MARKS DO NOT WRITE IN THIS MARGIN

ADDITIONAL SPACE FOR ANSWERS

ADDITIONAL SPACE FOR ANSWERS

FOR OFFICIAL USE

N5

National Qualifications
SPECIMEN ONLY

Mark

S847/75/02

Mathematics
Paper 2

Date — Not applicable

Duration — 1 hour 50 minutes

Fill in these boxes and read what is printed below.

Full name of centre

Town

Forename(s)

Surname

Number of seat

Date of birth

| Day | Month | Year | Scottish candidate number |

Total marks — 60

Attempt ALL questions.

You may use a calculator.

To earn full marks you must show your working in your answers.

State the units for your answer where appropriate.

Write your answers clearly in the spaces provided in this booklet. Additional space for answers is provided at the end of this booklet. If you use this space you must clearly identify the question number you are attempting.

Use **blue** or **black** ink.

Before leaving the examination room you must give this booklet to the Invigilator; if you do not, you may lose all the marks for this paper.

FORMULAE LIST

The roots of $ax^2 + bx + c = 0$ are $x = \dfrac{-b \pm \sqrt{(b^2 - 4ac)}}{2a}$

Sine rule: $\dfrac{a}{\sin A} = \dfrac{b}{\sin B} = \dfrac{c}{\sin C}$

Cosine rule: $a^2 = b^2 + c^2 - 2bc\cos A$ or $\cos A = \dfrac{b^2 + c^2 - a^2}{2bc}$

Area of a triangle: $A = \frac{1}{2}ab\sin C$

Volume of a sphere: $V = \frac{4}{3}\pi r^3$

Volume of a cone: $V = \frac{1}{3}\pi r^2 h$

Volume of a pyramid: $V = \frac{1}{3}Ah$

Standard deviation: $s = \sqrt{\dfrac{\Sigma(x - \bar{x})^2}{n - 1}}$

or $s = \sqrt{\dfrac{\Sigma x^2 - \dfrac{(\Sigma x)^2}{n}}{n - 1}}$, where n is the sample size.

MARKS | DO NOT WRITE IN THIS MARGIN

Total marks — 60

Attempt ALL questions

1. Beth normally cycles a total distance of 64 miles per week.

   She increases her total distance by 15% each week for the next three weeks.

   How many miles does she cycle in the third week?   **3**

   Give your answer to the nearest mile.

   $1.15^3 \times 64$

   $= 97.336$

   $= 97.3 \text{ m}$

2. There are 3×10^5 platelets per millilitre of blood.

   On average, a person has 5·5 litres of blood.

   On average, how many platelets does a person have in their blood?

   Give your answer in scientific notation.   **2**

   5500

   $= 300000$

   5500×300000

   $= 1650000000$

   $= 1.65 \times 10^9$

[Turn over

MARKS | DO NOT WRITE IN THIS MARGIN

3. Expand and simplify

$$(2x+3)(x^2-4x+1).$$

3

$2x^3 - 8x^2 + 2x + 3x^2 - 12x + 3$

$2x^3 - 5x^2 - 10x + 3$

4. The diagram shows a cube placed on top of a cuboid, relative to the coordinate axes.

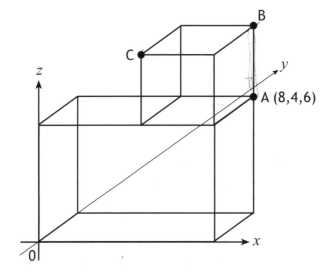

A is the point (8,4,6).

Write down the coordinates of B and C.

2

$B\ (8, 4, 9)$

$C\ (4, 0, 9)$

MARKS | DO NOT WRITE IN THIS MARGIN

5. In triangle PQR, PQ = 8 centimetres, QR = 3 centimetres and angle PQR = 120°.

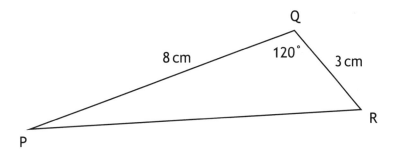

Calculate the length of PR. 3

$\cos A =$

~~$\cos a = b^4 + c^2 - a^2$~~

$\cos a^2 = b^2 + c^2 - 2bc \cos A$

$\cos a^2 = 8^2 + 3^2 - 2(8)(3)\cos 120$

$= \sqrt{97}$

$= 9.848857802$

$= 9.8 cm$

[Turn over

MARKS | DO NOT WRITE IN THIS MARGIN

6. A child's toy is in the shape of a hemisphere with a cone on top, as shown in the diagram.

17 cm

12 cm

The toy is 12 centimetres wide and 17 centimetres high.

Calculate the volume of the toy.

Give your answer correct to 2 significant figures.

5

$v = \frac{4}{3} \pi r^3 \div 2$

$= 904.7786842 \div 2$

$= 452.4 \, cm^3$

$V = \frac{1}{3} \times \pi r^2 h$

$= \frac{1}{3} \times \pi \, 6^2 \times 17$

$= 640.8842013$

$= 640.9 \, cm^3$

$452.4 + 640.9$

$= 1093.3 \, cm^3$

$= 1100 \, cm^3$

MARKS | DO NOT WRITE IN THIS MARGIN

7. Screenwash is available in bottles which are mathematically similar.

250 ml | 15 cm   36 cm

The smaller bottle has a height of 15 centimetres and a volume of 250 millilitres.

The larger bottle has a height of 36 centimetres.

Calculate the volume of the larger bottle.   3

$LSF = \dfrac{36}{15} \times 250$

$= 600^3$

$VSL = 600 \ cm^3$

$LSF = \dfrac{36}{15} = 2.4$

$2.4^3 \times 250$

~~*scribbled out*~~

$= 3456 \ ml$

[Turn over

8. Simplify $\dfrac{n^5 \times 10n}{2n^2}$.

3

MARKS

9. (a) A straight line has equation $4x + 3y = 12$.

Find the gradient of this line.   **2**

$3y = -4x + 12$

$\text{gradient} = -\dfrac{4}{3}$

(b) State the coordinates of the point where the line crosses the y-axis.   **1**

$0, 4$

[Turn over

10. The top of a table is in the shape of a regular hexagon.

The three diagonals of the hexagon, which are shown as dotted lines in the diagram below, each have length 40 centimetres.

Calculate the area of the top of the table.

4

MARKS | DO NOT WRITE IN THIS MARGIN

11. A cone is formed from a paper circle with a sector removed as shown.

The radius of the paper circle is 30 centimetres.

Angle AOB is 110°.

(a) Calculate the area of the sector removed from the circle. **3**

$$\frac{110}{360} \times 30^2 \times \pi$$

$$= 863.9378787$$

$$= 863.9$$

(b) Calculate the circumference of the base of the cone. **3**

$$C = \pi d$$

$$C = \pi \times$$

[Turn over

12. Part of the graph $y = 3\cos x° - 1$ is shown below.

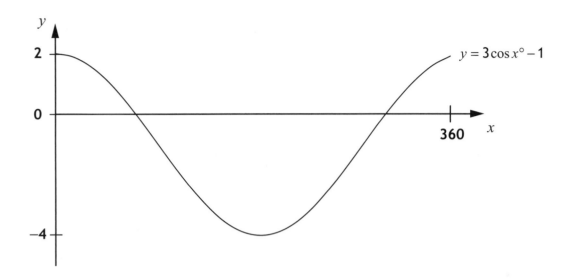

Calculate the x-coordinates of the points where the graph cuts the x-axis.   4

MARKS | DO NOT WRITE IN THIS MARGIN

13. Simplify $\dfrac{x^2 - 4x}{x^2 + x - 20}$.

3

[Turn over

MARKS | DO NOT WRITE IN THIS MARGIN

14. Change the subject of the formula $s = ut + \frac{1}{2}at^2$ to a.

3

MARKS | DO NOT WRITE IN THIS MARGIN

15. A yacht sails from a harbour H to a point C, then to a point D as shown below.

C is 50 kilometres due east of H.

D is on a bearing of 040° from C and is 79 kilometres from H.

(a) Calculate the size of angle CDH.　　　　　4

(b) Hence, calculate the bearing on which the yacht must sail to return directly to the harbour.　　　　　2

[Turn over

MARKS | DO NOT WRITE IN THIS MARGIN

16. A rectangular picture measuring 9 centimetres by 13 centimetres is placed on a rectangular piece of card.

The area of the card is 270 square centimetres.

There is a border x centimetres wide on all sides of the picture.

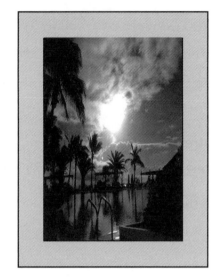

(a)   (i) Write down an expression for the length of the card in terms of x.   **1**

(ii) Hence show that $4x^2 + 44x - 153 = 0$.   **2**

MARKS | DO NOT WRITE IN THIS MARGIN

16. **(continued)**

(b) Calculate x, the width of the border.

Give your answer correct to one decimal place.   **4**

[END OF SPECIMEN QUESTION PAPER]

MARKS

ADDITIONAL SPACE FOR ANSWERS

NATIONAL 5

2018

FOR OFFICIAL USE

N5

National Qualifications 2018

Mark

X847/75/01

**Mathematics
Paper 1
(Non-Calculator)**

FRIDAY, 4 MAY
9:00 AM — 10:15 AM

Fill in these boxes and read what is printed below.

Full name of centre

Town

Forename(s)

Surname

Number of seat

Date of birth

Day　　Month　　Year　　Scottish candidate number

Total marks — 50

Attempt ALL questions.

You may NOT use a calculator.

To earn full marks you must show your working in your answers.

State the units for your answer where appropriate.

Write your answers clearly in the spaces provided in this booklet. Additional space for answers is provided at the end of this booklet. If you use this space you must clearly identify the question number you are attempting.

Use **blue** or **black** ink.

Before leaving the examination room you must give this booklet to the Invigilator; if you do not, you may lose all the marks for this paper.

FORMULAE LIST

The roots of $ax^2 + bx + c = 0$ are $x = \dfrac{-b \pm \sqrt{(b^2 - 4ac)}}{2a}$

Sine rule: $\dfrac{a}{\sin A} = \dfrac{b}{\sin B} = \dfrac{c}{\sin C}$

Cosine rule: $a^2 = b^2 + c^2 - 2bc\cos A$ or $\cos A = \dfrac{b^2 + c^2 - a^2}{2bc}$

Area of a triangle: $A = \frac{1}{2}ab\sin C$

Volume of a sphere: $V = \frac{4}{3}\pi r^3$

Volume of a cone: $V = \frac{1}{3}\pi r^2 h$

Volume of a pyramid: $V = \frac{1}{3}Ah$

Standard deviation: $s = \sqrt{\dfrac{\Sigma(x - \bar{x})^2}{n-1}}$

or $s = \sqrt{\dfrac{\Sigma x^2 - \dfrac{(\Sigma x)^2}{n}}{n-1}}$, where n is the sample size.

MARKS | DO NOT WRITE IN THIS MARGIN

Total marks — 50

Attempt ALL questions

1. Evaluate $2\frac{1}{3}+\frac{4}{5}$.

   2

   $$\frac{7}{3}+\frac{4}{5}$$

   $$\frac{35}{15}+\frac{12}{15}=\frac{47}{15}$$

2. Expand and simplify $(3x+1)(x-1)+2(x^2-5)$.

   3

   $$(3x+1)(x-1)+2x^2-10$$
   $$3x+3x^2+x-1+2x^2-10$$

   $$5x^2+4x-11$$

[Turn over

3. Solve, algebraically, the system of equations

$$4x + 5y = -3$$
$$6x - 2y = 5.$$

3

$4x + 5y = -3$ ①
$6x - 2y = 5$ ②
$30x - 10y = 25$ ②②×5
$8x + 10y = -6$ ④①×2

$38x = 19$

$x = 0.5$

sub $x = 0.5$ into ①

$4(0.5) + 5y = -3$
$2 + 5y = -3$
$5y = -5$
$y = -1$

$x = 0.5$
$y = -1$

4. Two vectors are given by $\mathbf{u} = \begin{pmatrix} 1 \\ 5 \\ 1 \end{pmatrix}$ and $\mathbf{u} + \mathbf{v} = \begin{pmatrix} 6 \\ -4 \\ 3 \end{pmatrix}$.

Find vector $\mathbf{v}$.

Express your answer in component form.

2

$$\begin{pmatrix} 6 \\ -4 \\ 3 \end{pmatrix} - \begin{pmatrix} 1 \\ 5 \\ 1 \end{pmatrix} = \begin{pmatrix} 5 \\ -9 \\ 2 \end{pmatrix}$$

MARKS | DO NOT WRITE IN THIS MARGIN

5. Solve

$$x^2 - 11x + 24 = 0.$$

2

6. Part of the graph of $y = a\cos bx°$ is shown in the diagram.

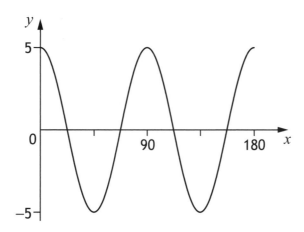

State the values of a and b.

2

$$a = 5$$
$$b = 4$$

[Turn over

MARKS | DO NOT WRITE IN THIS MARGIN

7. The cost of a journey with Tom's Taxis depends on the distance travelled.

The graph below shows the cost, P pounds, of a journey with Tom's Taxis against the distance travelled, d miles.

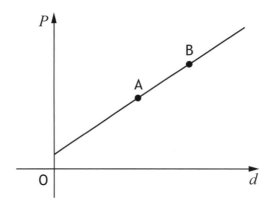

Point A represents a journey of 8 miles which costs £14.
Point B represents a journey of 12 miles which costs £20.

(a) Find the equation of the line in terms of P and d.

Give the equation in its simplest form.

3

MARKS DO NOT WRITE IN THIS MARGIN

7. (continued)

(b) Calculate the cost of a journey of 5 miles.   1

8. Determine the nature of the roots of the function $f(x) = 2x^2 + 4x + 5$.   2

$$b^2 - 4ac$$

$$16 - 4(2)(5)$$

$$16 - 40$$

$$-24$$

as $b^2 - 4ac$ is less than 0 there are no real roots

[Turn over

9. In the diagram shown below, ABCDEFGHJK is a regular decagon.
    - Angle KLJ is 17°.
    - AKL is a straight line.

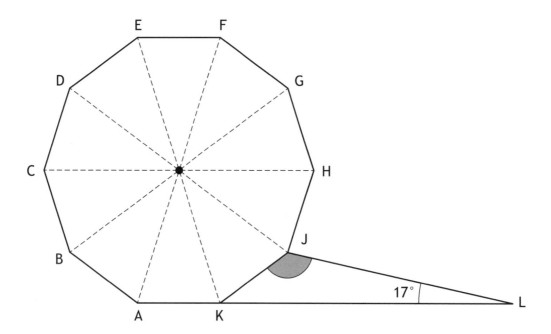

Calculate the size of shaded angle KJL.

2

MARKS | DO NOT WRITE IN THIS MARGIN

10. In triangle XYZ:

- XZ = 10 centimetres
- YZ = 8 centimetres
- $\cos Z = \dfrac{1}{8}$.

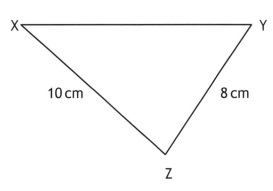

Calculate the length of XY.　　　3

$$\cos \hat{a} = b^2 + c^2 - 2bc \cos A$$
$$a^2 = 10^2 + 8^2 - 2 \times 10 \times 8 \cos \tfrac{1}{8}$$

$$100 + 64 - 160$$

[Turn over

MARKS DO NOT WRITE IN THIS MARGIN

11. Express $\dfrac{9}{\sqrt{6}}$ with a rational denominator.

Give your answer in its simplest form.

2

12. Given that $\cos 60° = 0 \cdot 5$, state the value of $\cos 240°$.

1

MARKS | DO NOT WRITE IN THIS MARGIN

13. The diagram shows a triangular prism, ABCDEF, relative to the coordinate axes.

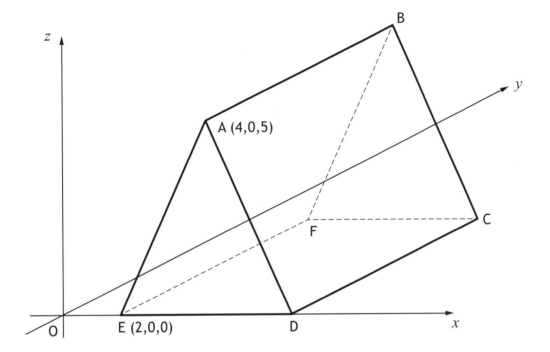

- AD = AE.
- DC = 8 units.
- Edges EF, DC and AB are parallel to the y-axis.

Write down the coordinates of B and C.   2

[Turn over

MARKS

14. Change the subject of the formula $y = g\sqrt{x} + h$ to x.   3

$$\sqrt{yg - h} = x$$

15. Remove the brackets and simplify $\left(\dfrac{2}{3}p^4\right)^2$.   2

$$\dfrac{4}{9}p^8$$

MARKS | DO NOT WRITE IN THIS MARGIN

16. Sketch the graph of $y = (x-6)(x+4)$.

On your sketch, show clearly the points of intersection with the x-axis and the y-axis, and the coordinates of the turning point.

3

$(6, 0) (-4, 0)$

$x^2 + 4x - 6x + 24$

$x^2 - 2x + 24$

$(0, 24)$

$(x - 1)^2 + 24 - 1$

$(x - 1)^2 + 23$

$1, 23$

[Turn over

MARKS | DO NOT WRITE IN THIS MARGIN

17. A square based pyramid is shown in the diagram below.

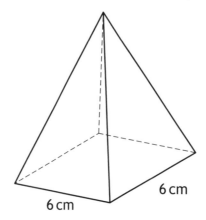

6 cm

6 cm

6 cm

The square base has length 6 centimetres.
The volume is 138 cubic centimetres.
Calculate the height of the pyramid.

3

$$V = \frac{1}{3} Ah$$

$$138 = \frac{1}{3} \times 36 \times h$$

$$138 = 12 \, h$$

$$h = 11.5 \, cm$$

MARKS | DO NOT WRITE IN THIS MARGIN

18. Express $\sin x° \cos x° \tan x°$ in its simplest form.

Show your working.

2

[Turn over

MARKS

19. **(a)** **(i)** Express $x^2 - 6x - 81$ in the form $(x - p)^2 + q$.

2

$(x - 3)^2 - 81 - 9$

$(x - 3)^2 - 90$

(ii) Hence state the equation of the axis of symmetry of the graph of $y = x^2 - 6x - 81$.

1

$(x - 3)^2$

MARKS | DO NOT WRITE IN THIS MARGIN

19. **(continued)**

(b) The roots of the equation $x^2 - 6x - 81 = 0$ can be expressed in the form $x = d \pm d\sqrt{e}$.

Find, algebraically, the values of d and e.   **4**

[END OF QUESTION PAPER]

ADDITIONAL SPACE FOR ANSWERS

MARKS | DO NOT WRITE IN THIS MARGIN

ADDITIONAL SPACE FOR ANSWERS

[BLANK PAGE]

DO NOT WRITE ON THIS PAGE

NATIONAL 5 MATHEMATICS   100   SQA EXAM PAPER 2018

FOR OFFICIAL USE

N5

National Qualifications 2018

Mark

X847/75/02

**Mathematics
Paper 2**

FRIDAY, 4 MAY

10:35 AM — 12:25 PM

Fill in these boxes and read what is printed below.

Full name of centre

Town

Forename(s)

Surname

Number of seat

Date of birth

| Day | Month | Year | Scottish candidate number |

Total marks — 60

Attempt ALL questions.

You may use a calculator.

To earn full marks you must show your working in your answers.

State the units for your answer where appropriate.

Write your answers clearly in the spaces provided in this booklet. Additional space for answers is provided at the end of this booklet. If you use this space you must clearly identify the question number you are attempting.

Use **blue** or **black** ink.

Before leaving the examination room you must give this booklet to the Invigilator; if you do not, you may lose all the marks for this paper.

FORMULAE LIST

The roots of $ax^2 + bx + c = 0$ are $x = \dfrac{-b \pm \sqrt{(b^2 - 4ac)}}{2a}$

Sine rule: $\dfrac{a}{\sin A} = \dfrac{b}{\sin B} = \dfrac{c}{\sin C}$

Cosine rule: $a^2 = b^2 + c^2 - 2bc\cos A$ or $\cos A = \dfrac{b^2 + c^2 - a^2}{2bc}$

Area of a triangle: $A = \frac{1}{2}ab\sin C$

Volume of a sphere: $V = \frac{4}{3}\pi r^3$

Volume of a cone: $V = \frac{1}{3}\pi r^2 h$

Volume of a pyramid: $V = \frac{1}{3}Ah$

Standard deviation: $s = \sqrt{\dfrac{\Sigma(x - \bar{x})^2}{n-1}}$

or $s = \sqrt{\dfrac{\Sigma x^2 - \dfrac{(\Sigma x)^2}{n}}{n-1}}$, where n is the sample size.

MARKS | DO NOT WRITE IN THIS MARGIN

Total marks — 60

Attempt ALL questions

1. Households in a city produced a total of 125 000 tonnes of waste in 2017.

   The total amount of waste is expected to fall by 2% each year.

   Calculate the total amount of waste these households are expected to produce in 2020.   **3**

   $$125000 \times 0.98^3$$

   $$= 117649 \text{ tonnes}$$

[Turn over

MARKS | DO NOT WRITE IN THIS MARGIN

2. The diagram below shows a sector of a circle, centre C.

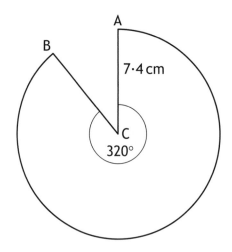

The radius of the circle is 7·4 centimetres.

Calculate the length of the major arc AB.

3

$$\frac{320}{360} \times \pi \times d$$

$$= \frac{320}{360} \times \pi \times 14.8$$

$$= 41.32939669$$

$$= 41.3 \, cm$$

3. Find $|\mathbf{r}|$, the magnitude of vector $\mathbf{r} = \begin{pmatrix} 24 \\ -12 \\ 8 \end{pmatrix}$.   **2**

$$\sqrt{24^2 - 12^2 \ 8^2}$$

$$= \sqrt{576 \ \text{—} \ 144 \ \text{—} \ 64}$$

$$= \ \ 28$$

4. Solve, algebraically, the inequation

$$3x < 6(x-1)-12.$$ **3**

$$3x < 6x - 6 - 12$$

$$-3x < -6 - 12$$

$$-x < -2 - 6$$

MARKS | DO NOT WRITE IN THIS MARGIN

5. A farmers' market took place one weekend.

Stallholders were asked to record the number of customers who visited their stall.

The number of customers who visited six of the stalls on Saturday were as follows:

$$120 \quad 126 \quad 125 \quad 131 \quad 130 \quad 124$$

(a) Calculate the mean and standard deviation of the number of customers. **4**

$$120 + 126 + 125 + 131 + 130 + 124$$

$$= 756 \div 6 = 126$$

x	$x - \bar{x}$	$(x - \bar{x})^2$
120	-6	36
126	0	0
125	-1	1
131	5	25
130	4	16
124	2	4
		$\Sigma\, 82$

$$Sd = \sqrt{\frac{\Sigma(x-x)^2}{n-1}}$$

$$= \sqrt{\frac{82}{5}}$$

$$= \underline{4}$$

MARKS | DO NOT WRITE IN THIS MARGIN

5. **(continued)**

The mean number of customers who visited these six stalls on Sunday was 117 and the standard deviation was 6·2.

(b) Make two valid comments comparing the number of customers who visited these stalls on Saturday and Sunday.   **2**

on average there were more people visiting the stalls on Sunday because Saturday had the mean of 126 and Sunday's mean was 117.

The amount of people visiting on Sunday was more varied as the standard deviation on Sunday was bigger by 2.2.

6. A function is defined as $f(x) = 5 + 4x$.

Given that $f(a) = 73$, calculate a.   **2**

$= 5 + 4(73)$

$= 297$

[Turn over

MARKS

7. A toy company makes juggling balls in the shape of a sphere with a diameter of 6·4 centimetres.

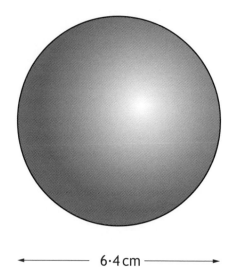

— 6·4 cm —

Calculate the volume of one juggling ball.

Give your answer correct to 2 significant figures.   3

$$V = \frac{4}{3}\pi r^3$$

$$= \frac{4}{3}\pi \times 3.2^3$$

$$= 137.2582774$$

$$= 140 \text{ cm}^3$$

MARKS

DO NOT WRITE IN THIS MARGIN

8. Solve the equation $7\sin x° + 2 = 3$, for $0 \le x < 360$.   3

[Turn over

MARKS | DO NOT WRITE IN THIS MARGIN

9. In this diagram:

- angle ABD = 75°
- angle BDC = 37°
- BC = 20 centimetres.

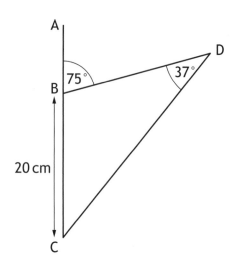

Calculate the length of DC.

3

MARKS | DO NOT WRITE IN THIS MARGIN

10. In the diagram below, $\overrightarrow{AB}$ and $\overrightarrow{EA}$ represent the vectors **u** and **w** respectively.

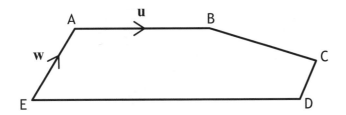

- $\overrightarrow{ED} = 2\overrightarrow{AB}$
- $\overrightarrow{EA} = 2\overrightarrow{DC}$

Express $\overrightarrow{BC}$ in terms of **u** and **w**.

Give your answer in its simplest form.

2

[Turn over

MARKS | DO NOT WRITE IN THIS MARGIN

11. Venus and Earth are two planets within our solar system.

Venus   Earth

The volume of Venus is approximately $9{\cdot}3 \times 10^{11}$ cubic kilometres.

This is 85% of the volume of Earth.

Calculate the volume of Earth.

3

85% = 930000000000

1.25 × 9300 000 00 000

 =

MARKS | DO NOT WRITE IN THIS MARGIN

12. The shape below is part of a circle, centre O.

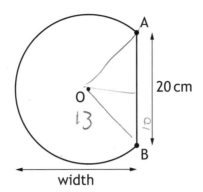

20 cm

O

13

A

B

width

The circle has radius 13 centimetres.

AB is a chord of length 20 centimetres.

Calculate the width of the shape.   **4**

$$13^2 - 10^2$$

$$= \sqrt{69}$$

$$= 8.306623863$$

$$= 8.3 + 13$$

$$= 21.3 cm$$

[Turn over

MARKS | DO NOT WRITE IN THIS MARGIN

13. A ferry and a trawler receive a request for help from a stranded yacht.

On the diagram the points F, T and Y show the positions of the ferry, the trawler and the yacht respectively.

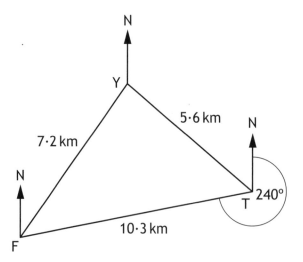

- FY is 7·2 kilometres.
- TY is 5·6 kilometres.
- FT is 10·3 kilometres.
- F is on a bearing of 240° from T.

Calculate the bearing of the yacht from the trawler.   4

MARKS | DO NOT WRITE IN THIS MARGIN

14. A straight line has equation $2x - 5y = 20$.

Find the coordinates of the point where this line crosses the y-axis.   **2**

15. Express

$$\frac{n}{n^2 - 4} \div \frac{3}{n-2}, \quad n \neq -2, n \neq 2$$

as a single fraction in its simplest form.   **3**

[Turn over

MARKS | DO NOT WRITE IN THIS MARGIN

16. Chris wants to store his umbrella in a locker.

The locker is a cuboid with internal dimensions of length 40 centimetres, breadth 40 centimetres and height 70 centimetres.

The umbrella is 85 centimetres long.

He thinks it will fit into the locker from corner P to corner M.

Is he correct?

Justify your answer.   4

11. • $85\% = 9\cdot3\times10^{11}$

   • $1\% = \dfrac{9\cdot3\times10^{11}}{85}$

   • $1\cdot094...\times10^{12}$ (km³)

   or 1094117647000 (km³)

12. **Method 1**

   •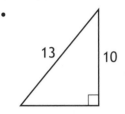

   • $x^2 = 13^2 - 10^2$

   • $x = 8\cdot3(...)$

   • width = $21\cdot3(...$ cm)

Method 2

   •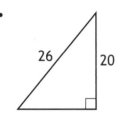

   • $x^2 = 26^2 - 20^2$

   • $x = 16\cdot6\,(...)$

   • width = $21\cdot3\,(...$ cm)

13. • $\dfrac{10\cdot3^2 + 5\cdot6^2 - 7\cdot2^2}{2\times10\cdot3\times5\cdot6}$

   • $\cos YTF = \dfrac{85\cdot61}{115\cdot36}\,(=0\cdot742...)$

   • angle YTF = $42(\cdot088...)$

   • bearing = $282(\cdot088...)$

14. **Method 1**

   • $-5y = ... + 20$ or $... - 20 = 5y$

   or $\dfrac{2x}{5} - \dfrac{5y}{5} = \dfrac{20}{5}$

   • coordinates = (0, −4)

Method 2

   • $2\times0 - 5y = 20$

   • coordinates = (0, −4)

15. • $\dfrac{n}{n^2 - 4} \times \dfrac{n-2}{3}$

   • $n^2 - 4 = (n+2)(n-2)$

   • $\dfrac{n}{3(n+2)}$ or $\dfrac{n}{3n+6}$ S

16. • $40^2 + 40^2$ or $40^2 + 70^2$

   • $\sqrt{40^2 + 40^2 + 70^2}$

   • 90

   • Yes, since 85 < 90

17. • $\dfrac{1}{2}\times38\times55\times\sin75\;(=1009\cdot39...)$

   • $\dfrac{75}{360}$

   • $\dfrac{75}{360}\times\pi\times30^2\;(=589\cdot04...)$

   • evidence of area of triangle − area of sector

   • $420\,(\cdot3...)$ cm²

18. (a) **Method 1**

   •¹ e.g. $\dfrac{24}{16}$ or equivalent

   •² $576\times\left(\dfrac{24}{16}\right)^3$

   •³ $1944 \neq 1125$, so the cartons are not similar

Method 2

   •¹ e.g. $\dfrac{16}{24}$ or equivalent

   •² $576\div\left(\dfrac{16}{24}\right)^3$

   •³ $1944 \neq 1125$, so the cartons are not similar

Method 3

   • e.g. volume scale factor = $\dfrac{1125}{576}$ or equivalent

   • $\sqrt[3]{\dfrac{1125}{576}}\times16$

   • $20 \neq 24$, so the cartons are not similar

Method 4

- e.g. linear scale factor = $\dfrac{24}{16}$ or equivalent

- $\left(\dfrac{24}{16}\right)^3$ and $\dfrac{1125}{576}$

- $3 \cdot 375 \neq 1 \cdot 95\ldots$, so the cartons are not similar

Method 5

- e.g. volume scale factor = $\dfrac{1125}{576}$ or equivalent

- $\sqrt[3]{\dfrac{1125}{576}}$ and $\dfrac{24}{16}$

- $1 \cdot 25 \neq 1 \cdot 5$, so the cartons are not similar

(b) **Method 1**

- volume scale factor = $\dfrac{1500}{576}$

- $\sqrt[3]{\dfrac{1500}{576}} \times 16 = 22\ (\cdot 0\ldots\ \text{cm})$

Method 2

- volume scale factor = $\dfrac{576}{1500}$

- $16 \div \sqrt[3]{\dfrac{576}{1500}} = 22\ (\cdot 0\ldots\ \text{cm})$

MARKS

17. In the diagram below AOD is a sector of a circle, with centre O, and BOC is a triangle.

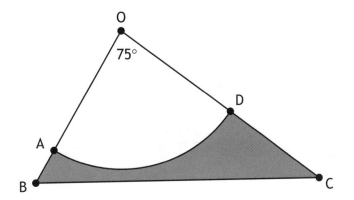

In sector AOD:

- radius = 30 centimetres
- angle AOD = 75°.

In triangle OBC:

- OB = 38 centimetres
- OC = 55 centimetres.

Calculate the area of the shaded region, ABCD.

5

[Turn over

18. A cinema sells popcorn in two different sized cartons.

16 cm

24 cm

The small carton is 16 centimetres deep and has a volume of 576 cubic centimetres.

The large carton is 24 centimetres deep and has a volume of 1125 cubic centimetres.

(a) Show that the two cartons are **not** mathematically similar.   **3**

large popcorn

$LSF = \dfrac{24}{16} \times 576$

864

$VSI = \left(\dfrac{24}{16}\right)^3 \times 576$

$= 1944$

$1944 \neq 1125$ so they are not mathematically similar

MARKS DO NOT WRITE IN THIS MARGIN

18. **(continued)**

The large carton is redesigned so that the two cartons are **now** mathematically similar.

The volume of the redesigned large carton is 1500 cubic centimetres.

(b) Calculate the depth of the redesigned large carton.   2

[END OF QUESTION PAPER]

ADDITIONAL SPACE FOR ANSWERS

ADDITIONAL SPACE FOR ANSWERS

MARKS | DO NOT WRITE IN THIS MARGIN

[BLANK PAGE]

DO NOT WRITE ON THIS PAGE

NATIONAL 5

Answers

NATIONAL 5 MATHEMATICS 2017

One mark is available for each •. There are no half marks.

Paper 1

1. • $(-5)^2 + 3 \times (-5)$
   • 10

2. • 218, 250
   • 16

3. • $\dfrac{11}{6} \times \dfrac{4}{3}$
   • $\dfrac{22}{9}$ or $2\dfrac{4}{9}$

4. • evidence of any 3 correct terms
     e.g. $2x^3 - 8x^2 + 2x$
   • $2x^3 - 8x^2 + 2x + 3x^2 - 12x + 3$
   • $2x^3 - 5x^2 - 10x + 3$

5. • Coordinate B (0,6,6)
   • Coordinate C (3,3,9)

6. **Method 1:** $y - b = m(x - a)$
   • $-\dfrac{8}{4}$ or equivalent
   • e.g. $y - (-2) = -\dfrac{8}{4}(x - 3)$
   • $y = -2x + 4$ or equivalent

   Method 2: $y = mx + c$
   • $-\dfrac{8}{4}$
   • e.g. $-2 = -\dfrac{8}{4} \times 3 + c$
   • $y = -2x + 4$ or equivalent

7. • $\dfrac{1}{2} \times 12 \times 8 \times \dfrac{2}{3}$
   • 32 (cm)^2

8. • $3x - 6$
   • $-2x > -10$ or $10 > 2x$
   • $x < 5$ or $5 > x$

9. **Method 1**
   • OBD = 32
   • ODB = 32
   • CAB = 26

   Method 2
   • ABC = 32
   • OCB = 58
   • CAB = 26

10. • $Fc = t^2 + 4b$
    • $4b = Fc - t^2$
    • $b = \dfrac{Fc - t^2}{4}$

11. • $\dfrac{}{a^2}$ or $\dfrac{}{a^3}$ or $\dfrac{}{a^2 \times a}$
    • $\dfrac{3 - 2a}{a^2}$

12. **Method 1**
    • $\bar{x} = 4$
    • 9, 0, 4, 1, 4
    • $\sqrt{\dfrac{18}{4}}$
    • $a = 3$, $b = 2$ or $\dfrac{3\sqrt{2}}{2}$

    Method 2
    • $\sum x = 20$ and $\sum x^2 = 98$
    • $\sqrt{\dfrac{98 - \dfrac{20^2}{5}}{5 - 1}}$
    • $\sqrt{\dfrac{18}{4}}$
    • $a = 3$, $b = 2$ or $\dfrac{3\sqrt{2}}{2}$

13. • e.g. $\begin{array}{l} 9x - 3y = 6 \\ x + 3y = 19 \end{array}$
    • values for x and y
    • $x = 2\cdot 5$, $y = 5\cdot 5$

14. (a) • $a = 5$

(b) • $8 = (-3 + 5)^2 + b$

• $b = 4$

15. Method 1

• $\dfrac{5}{7}$ or $\dfrac{7}{5}$

• $(x =) \dfrac{5}{7}(x + 2 \cdot 6)$

or $\dfrac{7}{5}x = x + 2 \cdot 6$

• $x = 6 \cdot 5$

Method 2

• $\dfrac{x}{5} = \dfrac{x + 2 \cdot 6}{7}$ or equivalent

• $7x = 5(x + 2 \cdot 6)$ or equivalent

• $x = 6 \cdot 5$

Method 3

• $5 : 2 \equiv x : 2 \cdot 6$ stated or implied by

• $2 \cdot 6 \times \dfrac{5}{2}$

• $x = 6 \cdot 5$

Method 4

• $\dfrac{2}{7}PR = 2 \cdot 6$

• $PR = \dfrac{7}{2} \times 2 \cdot 6 \quad (= 9 \cdot 1)$

• $x = (9 \cdot 1 - 2 \cdot 6 =) 6 \cdot 5$

Paper 2

1. • $18^2 + (-14)^2 + 3^2$

• 23

2. • $\times 1 \cdot 045$

• $1200 \times 1 \cdot 045^3$

• £1369

3. • $180^2 + 250^2 - 2 \times 180 \times 250 \times \cos 147$

• $170380 \cdot 3$

• $412 \cdot 77 \ldots (m) \quad / \ 413\,m$

4. • $\dfrac{-5 \pm \sqrt{5^2 - 4 \times 2 \times (-4)}}{2 \times 2}$

• 57 (stated or implied)

• $x = -3 \cdot 1, \ x = 0 \cdot 6$

5. • $115\% = 4830$

• $1\% = \dfrac{4830}{115}$ or equivalent

• 4200

6. • evidence of difference in two volumes

• $\dfrac{4}{3} \times \pi \times 12^3 \ (= 7238 \cdot 229 \ldots)$

• $\dfrac{4}{3} \times \pi \times 9^3 \ (= 3053 \cdot 628 \ldots)$

• $4184 \cdot 601$

• $4180\,mm^3$

7. Method 1

• $8^2 + 19^2$ and 22^2

• $8^2 + 19^2 = 425, \ 22^2 = 484$

• $8^2 + 19^2 \neq 22^2$; No

Method 2

• $8^2 + 19^2$

• length of longest side $= 20 \cdot 6$

• $20 \cdot 6 \neq 22$; No

Method 3

• $\cos x° = \dfrac{8^2 + 19^2 - 22^2}{2 \times 8 \times 19}$

• $\cos x° = -0 \cdot 194$

• $(x =) \ 101 \cdot 2$; No

Method 4

• $\cos x° = \dfrac{8^2 + 7^2 - 6^2}{2 \times 8 \times 7}$

and $\cos y° = \dfrac{7^2 + 19^2 - 16^2}{2 \times 7 \times 19}$

• $\cos x° = 0 \cdot 6875$ and $\cos y° = 0 \cdot 5789$

• $(\text{sum} =) \ 101 \cdot 2$; No

8. (a) • $\mathbf{d}-\mathbf{c}$ or equivalent

(b) • $\overrightarrow{TP}+\dfrac{1}{2}\overrightarrow{PR}$ or $\overrightarrow{TQ}+\overrightarrow{QR}+\dfrac{1}{2}\overrightarrow{RP}$

• $\dfrac{3}{2}\mathbf{d}-\dfrac{1}{2}\mathbf{c}$ or equivalent

9. (a) • $(2x-5)(2x+5)$

(b) • $(2x\ \ 5)(x\ \ 2)$

• $(2x-5)(x+2)$

• $\dfrac{2x+5}{x+2}$

10. • 40 and 104

• $\dfrac{DF}{\sin 40}=\dfrac{15}{\sin 104}$

• $\dfrac{15\times\sin 40}{\sin 104}$

• $9\cdot9(36...)$ km

11. • $-5y=-3x...$ or $3x...=5y$ or

or $\dfrac{3x}{5}-\dfrac{5y}{5}-\dfrac{10}{5}=0$

• $\dfrac{3}{5}$ or $0\cdot6$

12. • $\dfrac{1}{x^{\frac{1}{3}}}$ stated or implied

• $x^{-\frac{1}{3}}$

13. •

• $x^2=14^2-12^2$

• $7\cdot2$

• $42\cdot4$ cm

14. Method 1

• $\dfrac{\text{angle}}{360}\times\pi\times12\cdot8$

• $\dfrac{31\cdot5\times360}{\pi\times12\cdot8}$

• $282°$

Method 2

• $\dfrac{31\cdot5}{\pi\times12\cdot8}$ $(=0\cdot78...)$

• $\dfrac{31\cdot5\times360}{\pi\times12\cdot8}$

• $282°$

15. (a) • $51\cdot5$ m

(b) • 17 m

(c) • $61=40+23\cos x$

• $\cos x=\dfrac{21}{23}$

• $24(\cdot07...)-24\cdot1°$

• $335(\cdot92...)-\mathbf{335\cdot9°}$

NATIONAL 5 MATHEMATICS 2017 SPECIMEN QUESTION PAPER

One mark is available for each •. There are no half marks.

Paper 1

1. • $\dfrac{19}{8} \times \dfrac{16}{5}$

   • $7\dfrac{3}{5}$ or $\dfrac{38}{5}$

2. • $11 - 2 - 6x < 39$

   • $-6x < 30$ or $-30 < 6x$

   • $x > -5$ or $-5 < x$

3. • $\begin{pmatrix} 9 \\ -1 \\ -4 \end{pmatrix}$

   • $\sqrt{9^2 + (-1)^2 + (-4)^2}$

   • $7\sqrt{2}$

4. • $45 = a(-3)^2$ or equivalent

   • $a = 5$

5. • 53 $\quad [5^2 - 4 \times 7 \times (-1)]$

   • two real and distinct roots

6. (a) • $\dfrac{240}{12}$ or equivalent

   • $y - 100 = \dfrac{240}{12}(x - 3)$

   or $y - 340 = \dfrac{240}{12}(x - 15)$

   or $100 = \dfrac{240}{12} \times 3 + c$

   or $340 = \dfrac{240}{12} \times 15 + c$

   • $W = 20A + 40$ or equivalent

   (b) • $20 \times 12 + 40 = 280 \text{kg}$

7. (a) • median = 19·5

   • quartiles = 17 and 26

   • SIQR = 4·5

   (b) • On average the second round's scores are higher

   • The second round's scores are more consistent.

8. (a) • $5a + 3c = 158 \cdot 25$

   (b) • $3a + 2c = 98$

   (c) • e.g. $\begin{aligned} 10a + 6c &= 316 \cdot 50 \\ 9a + 6c &= 294 \end{aligned}$

   • values for a and c

   • $a = 22 \cdot 5$ and $c = 15 \cdot 25$

   • Adult £22·50
     Child £15·25

9. • $80\% = 480000$

   • $10\% = 60000$ or equivalent

   • 600000

10. • $\dfrac{2}{\sqrt{5}}$

    • $\dfrac{2\sqrt{5}}{5}$

11. (a) • $\mathbf{b} - \mathbf{a}$ or $-\mathbf{a} + \mathbf{b}$

    (b) • $2(\mathbf{b} - \mathbf{a})$ or $2(-\mathbf{a} + \mathbf{b})$

12. • $a = 4$

    • $b = 3$

13. (a) • $(x - 4)^2 \dots\dots\dots$

    • $(x - 4)^2 + 3$

    (b)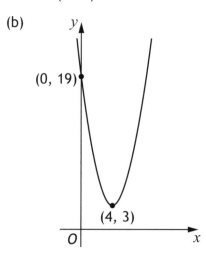

14. • $(x + 2)(x - 4)$

    • $4(x - 4) - 3(x + 2)$

    • $\dfrac{x - 22}{(x + 2)(x - 4)}$

15. • $\dfrac{\sin x}{\cos x}$ or $\dfrac{\sin^2 x}{\cos^2 x}$

• $\dfrac{\sin^2 x}{\cos^2 x} \times \cos^2 x = \sin^2 x$

16. (a) • $r - 5$

(b) • $r^2 = (r-5)^2 + 9^2$

• $r^2 = r^2 - 10r + 25 + 81$

• $r = 10 \cdot 6$

Paper 2

1. • $\times 1 \cdot 15$

• $64 \times 1 \cdot 15^3$

• 97 miles

2. • $3 \times 10^5 \times 5 \cdot 5 \times 1000$

• $1 \cdot 65 \times 10^9$

3. • e.g. $2x^3 - 8x^2 + 2x \dots$

• e.g. $\dots 3x^2 - 12x + 3$

• $2x^3 - 5x^2 - 10x + 3$

4. • $B(8, 4, 10)$

• $C(4, 0, 10)$

5. • $(PR^2 =) 8^2 + 3^2 - 2 \times 8 \times 3 \times \cos 120°$

• 97

• $9 \cdot 8 \ (488\dots)$ cm

6. • $\dfrac{1}{3} \times \pi \times 6^2 \times 11 (= 414 \cdot 690\dots)$

• $\dfrac{4}{3} \times \pi \times 6^3 (= 904 \cdot 778\dots)$ **or**

  $\dfrac{1}{2} \times \dfrac{4}{3} \times \pi \times 6^3 (= 452 \cdot 389\dots)$

• evidence

• $867 \cdot 079\dots$

• 870 cm³

7. • $\dfrac{36}{15} \ (= 2 \cdot 4)$

• $\left(\dfrac{36}{15}\right)^3 \times 250 \ (= 2 \cdot 4^3 \times 250)$

• 3456 ml

8. • $10n^6$

• $\dfrac{5n^6}{n^2}$

• $5n^4$

9. (a) • $3y = -4x + 12$

• gradient $= -\dfrac{4}{3}$

(b) • $(0, 4)$

10. • 60

• $\dfrac{1}{2} \times 20 \times 20 \times \sin 60$

• $\left(\dfrac{1}{2} \times 20 \times 20 \times \sin 60\right) \times 6$

• 1039·2 cm²

11. (a) • $\dfrac{110}{360}$

• $\dfrac{110}{360} \times \pi \times 30^2$

• $863 \cdot 9\dots$ / 864 cm²

(b) • $\dfrac{250}{360}$

• $\dfrac{250}{360} \times \pi \times 60$

• $130 \cdot 8\dots$ / 131 cm

12. • $3\cos x - 1 = 0$

• $\cos x = \dfrac{1}{3}$

• $70 \cdot 5$

• $289 \cdot 5$

13. • $x(x - 4)$

• $(x - 4)(x + 5)$

• $\dfrac{x}{x + 5}$

14. • $s - ut = \dfrac{1}{2}at^2$

• $2(s - ut) = at^2$

• $a = \dfrac{2(s - ut)}{t^2}$

15. (a) • 130°

• $\dfrac{50}{\sin \text{CDH}} = \dfrac{79}{\sin 130}$

• $\sin \text{CDH} = \dfrac{50 \sin 130}{79}$

• **29°**

(b) • 40

• 249 $[180 + 40 + 29]$ / 249°

16. (a) (i) • $2x + 13$

(ii) • $(2x + 13)(2x + 9) = 4x^2 + 44x + 117$

• $4x^2 + 44x + 117 = 270$

$\Rightarrow 4x^2 + 44x - 153 = 0$

(b) • $\dfrac{-44 \pm \sqrt{44^2 - 4 \times 4 \times (-153)}}{2 \times 4}$

• $\dfrac{-44 \pm \sqrt{4384}}{2 \times 4}$

(stated or implied)

• 2·77... and −13·77...

• 2·8 cm

NATIONAL 5 MATHEMATICS 2018

One mark is available for each •. There are no half marks.

Paper 1

1. • $2\dfrac{\cdots}{15}+\dfrac{\cdots}{15}$ or $\dfrac{\cdots}{15}+\dfrac{\cdots}{15}$

    • $3\dfrac{2}{15}$ or $\dfrac{47}{15}$

2. • $3x^2-3x+x-1$ **or** $2x^2-10$

    • $3x^2-3x+x-1+2x^2-10$

    • $5x^2-2x-11$

3. • e.g. $\begin{aligned}8x+10y&=-6\\30x-10y&=25\end{aligned}$

    • values for x and y

    • $x=0\cdot5$, $y=-1$

4. • e.g. $\begin{pmatrix}6\\-4\\3\end{pmatrix}-\begin{pmatrix}1\\5\\1\end{pmatrix}$

    • $\begin{pmatrix}5\\-9\\2\end{pmatrix}$

5. • $(x-3)(x-8)$

    • $(x=)\,3$, $(x=)\,8$

6. • $a=5$

    • $b=4$

7. (a) **Method 1**

    • $\dfrac{6}{4}$ or equivalent

    • e.g. $y-20=\dfrac{6}{4}(x-12)$

    • $P=\dfrac{3}{2}d+2$ or equivalent

    Method 2

    • $\dfrac{6}{4}$ or equivalent

    • e.g. $20=\dfrac{6}{4}\times12+c$

    • $P=\dfrac{3}{2}d+2$ or equivalent

    (b) • (£) 9·50

8. • -24

    • no real roots

9. • interior angle $=72+72$

    or JKL $=36$

    • 127

10. • $10^2+8^2-2\times10\times8\times\dfrac{1}{8}$

    • $XY^2=144$

    • XY $=12$ (cm)

11. • $\dfrac{9\sqrt{6}}{6}$

    • $\dfrac{3\sqrt{6}}{2}$

12. • $-0\cdot5$

13. • coordinates of B(4, 8, 5)

    • coordinates of C(6, 8, 0)

14. • $y-h=g\sqrt{x}$

    • $\sqrt{x}=\dfrac{y-h}{g}$

    • $x=\left(\dfrac{y-h}{g}\right)^2$

15. • $\dfrac{4}{9}$ or p^8

    • $\dfrac{4}{9}p^8$

16. • -4 **AND** 6

    • (1, −25) **OR** −24

    • turning point $=(1, -25)$ **AND** y-intercept $=-24$ and consistently annotated parabola.

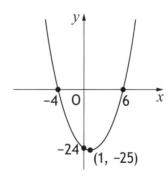

17. **Method 1**

    • $\dfrac{1}{3}\times6^2\times h$ or $\dfrac{1}{3}Ah=138$

    • $\dfrac{1}{3}\times6^2\times h=138$

    • 11·5 (cm)

Method 2

- $\dfrac{3V}{A}$ or $\dfrac{V}{\frac{1}{3}A}$

- $\dfrac{3 \times 138}{6 \times 6}$ or $\dfrac{138}{\frac{1}{3} \times 6 \times 6}$

- 11·5 (cm)

18.
- $\sin x \cos x \dfrac{\sin x}{\cos x}$
- $\sin^2 x$

19. (a) (i)
- $(x-3)^2 \ldots$
    - $(x-3)^2 - 90$

    (ii) • $x = 3$

(b)

Method 1

- $(x-3)^2 - 90 = 0$
- $x - 3 = \pm\sqrt{90}$
- $x = 3 \pm \sqrt{90}$
- $d = 3,\ e = 10$ or $3 \pm 3\sqrt{10}$

Method 2

- $\dfrac{6 \pm \sqrt{(-6)^2 - 4 \times 1 \times (-81)}}{2 \times 1}$

- discriminant = 360 (stated or implied)
- discriminant = $6\sqrt{10}$
- $d = 3,\ e = 10$ or $3 \pm 3\sqrt{10}$

Paper 2

1. • $\times 0 \cdot 98$

- $125\,000 \times 0 \cdot 98^3$
- $117\,649$ (tonnes)

2. **Method 1**

- $\dfrac{320}{360}$

- $\dfrac{320}{360} \times 2 \times \pi \times 7 \cdot 4$

- $41(\cdot 32\ldots)$ (cm)

Method 2

- $\dfrac{360}{320}$

- $2 \times \pi \times 7 \cdot 4 \div \dfrac{360}{320}$

- $41(\cdot 32\ldots)$ (cm)

3. • $24^2 + (-12)^2 + 8^2$

- 28

4. • $3x < 6x - 6 - 12$

- $-3x < -18$ or $18 < 3x$

- $x > 6$ or $6 < x$

5. (a) **Method 1**

- mean = 126

- $(x - \bar{x})^2 = 36,\ 0,\ 1,\ 25,\ 16,\ 4$

- $\sqrt{\dfrac{82}{5}}$

- $4(\cdot 049\ldots)$

Method 2

- 126

- $\sum x = 756$ and $\sum x^2 = 95338$

- $\sqrt{\dfrac{95338 - \dfrac{756^2}{6}}{5}}$

- $4(\cdot 049\ldots)$

(b) • e.g. on average the number of customers was higher on Saturday

- e.g. the number of customers was less varied on Saturday

6. • $5 + 4a = 73$ or $5 + 4 \times 17$

- $(a =)\,17$

7. • $\dfrac{4}{3} \times \pi \times 3 \cdot 2^3$

- volume = $137 \cdot 2\ldots$

- $140\,(\text{cm}^3)$

8. • $\sin x = \dfrac{1}{7}$

- $8 \cdot 2(1\ldots)$

- $171 \cdot 8$ or $171 \cdot 7(8\ldots)$

9. • $\dfrac{20}{\sin 37} = \dfrac{DC}{\sin 105}$

- $\dfrac{20 \sin 105}{\sin 37}$

- $32\ (\cdot 1\ldots\ \text{cm})$

10. • $\overrightarrow{ED} = 2\mathbf{u}$ and $\overrightarrow{DC} = \dfrac{1}{2}\mathbf{w}$

- $\mathbf{u} - \dfrac{1}{2}\mathbf{w}$